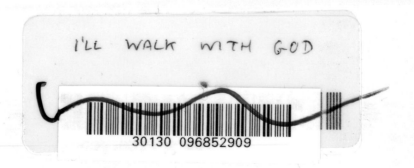

Wise Publications
New York/London/Sydney

"I'll Walk With God"

Exclusive Distributors:
Music Sales Limited,
78 Newman Street,
London W1P 3LA.
Music Sales Pty Limited,
27 Clarendon Street,
Artarmon, Sydney,
Australia 2064.

M3.431

CM28704

£2.95

"I'll Walk With God"

Music compiled by Peter Foss.
Cover painting "The Light of The World"
by William Holman Hunt.
Book designed by Pearce Marchbank.

"Onward Christian Soldiers"

By A. Sullivan and S. Baring Gould.

(For Organ: Registration No. 5)

CHORUS

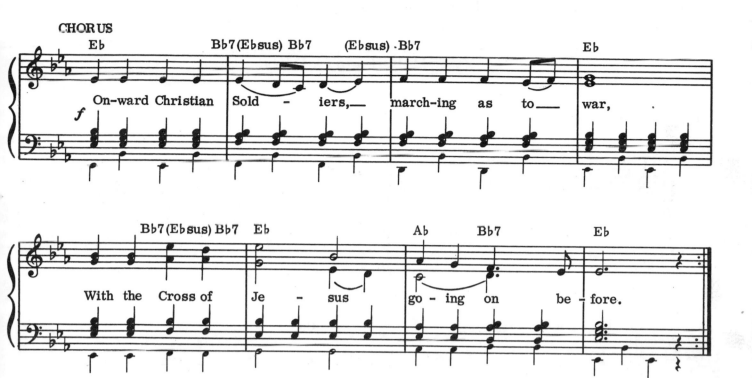

On-ward Christian Sold - iers,__ march-ing as to__ war,
With the Cross of Je - sus go - ing on be - fore.

2. At the name of Jesus Satan's host doth flee,
    On then, Christian soldiers, on to victory:
    Hell's foundations quiver at the shout of praise;
    Brothers, lift your voices, loud your anthems raise.

        Chorus.

3. Like a mighty army moves the Church of God.
    Brothers, we are treading where the saints have trod.
    We are not divided, all one body we,
    One in hope and purpose, one in charity.

        Chorus.

4. Crowns and thrones may perish, kingdoms rise and wane,
    But the Church of Jesus constant will remain:
    Gates of hell can never 'gainst that Church prevail;
    We have Christ's own promise, and that cannot fail.

        Chorus.

5. Onward, then, ye people, join our happy throng,
    Blend with ours your voices in the triumph song:
    "Glory, praise, and honour unto Christ the King!"
    This through countless ages men and angels sing.

        Chorus.

"Jerusalem"

By C. Hubert and H. Parry.

(For Organ: Registration No. 7)

"Hallelujah" (From 'The Messiah')

By Handel.

(For Organ: Registration No. 5)

lu - jah, Hal-le - lu - jah, Hal-le - lu - jah, Hal-le - lu - jah,

For the Lord God om - ni - po - tent reign - eth Hal - le-

- lu - jah, Hal-le-lu - jah, Hal-le - lu - jah, Hal-le - lu - jah.

The King - dom of this world

Is be - come the King - dom of our

"Lead Kindly Light"

By C. H. Purday.

(For Organ: Registration No. 3)

2. I was not ever thus, nor prayed that Thou
    Shouldst lead me on;
I loved to choose and see my path, but now
    Lead Thou me on;
I loved the garish day, and, spite of fears,
Pride ruled my will; remember not past years.

3. So long Thy power hath blessed me, sure it still
    Will lead me on
O'er moor and fen, o'er crag and torrent, till
    The night is gone,
And with the morn those angel faces smile
Which I have loved long since, and lost awhile.

"O God Our Help"

By Dr. Crofts.

(For Organ: Registration No. 5)

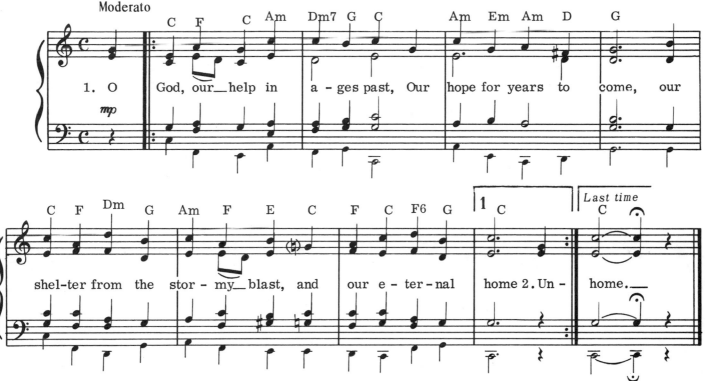

2. Under the shadow of Thy throne
   Thy saints have dwelt secure;
   Sufficient is Thine arm alone,
   And our defence is sure.

3. Before the hills in order stood,
   Or earth received her frame,
   From everlasting Thou art God,
   To endless years the same.

4. A thousand ages in Thy sight
   Are like an evening gone,
   Short as the watch that ends the night
   Before the rising sun.

5. Time, like an ever-rolling stream,
   Bears all its sons away,
   They fly forgotten, as a dream
   Dies at the opening day.

6. O God our help in ages past,
   Our hope for years to come,
   Be Thou our guard while troubles last,
   And our eternal home.

"The Day Thou Gave'st Lord Is Ended"

By C. C. Scholefield.

(For Organ: Registration No. 3)

2. We thank Thee that Thy church unsleeping,
While earth rolls onward into light,
Through all the world her watch is keeping,
And rests not now by day or night.

3. As o'er each continent and island
The dawn leads on to another day,
The voice of prayer is never silent,
Nor dies the strain of praise away.

4. The sun that bids us rest is waking
Our brethren 'neath the western sky,
And hour by hour fresh lips are making
Thy wondrous doings heard on high.

5. So be it, Lord: Thy throne shall never
Like earth's proud empires, pass away;
Thy kingdom stands, and grows forever
Till all Thy creatures own Thy sway.

"The Lost Chord"

By A. Sullivan
and Adelaide A. Proctor.

(For Organ: Registration No. 5)

16

"Amazing Grace"

Traditional,
adapted by Judy Collins.

(For Organ: Registration No. 4)

19

"I'll Walk Beside You"

Words by Edward Lockton.
Music by Alan Murray.

20

"Abide With Me"

By W. H. Monk.

(For Organ: Registration No. 3)

2. Swift to its close ebbs out life's little day;
   Earth's joys grow dim, its glories pass away;
   Change and decay in all around I see:
   O Thou who changest not, abide with me.

3. I need Thy presence ev'ry passing hour;
   What but Thy grace can foil the tempter's power?
   Who like Thyself my guide and stay can be?
   Through cloud and sunshine, O abide with me.

4. I fear no foe, with Thee at hand to bless;
   Ills have no weight and tears no bitterness:
   Where is death's sting? where, grave, thy victory?
   I triumph still if Thou abide with me.

5. Hold Thou Thy cross before my closing eyes,
   Shine through the gloom and point me to the skies;
   Heaven's morning breaks, and earth's vain shadows
   In life, in death, O Lord, abide with me.   [flee:

"God Bless The Child"

Words and music by
Arthur Herzog Jr. and Billie Holiday.

(For Organ: Registration No.3)

weak ones fade, emp-ty pock-ets don't ev-er make the grade;__

ma-ma may have, pa-pa may have, but God bless the child that's

got his own! That's got his own.

Mo - ney, you got lot's o' friends,

crowd-in' round the

door,

When you're gone and

spend-in' ends,__

25

"Let There Be Peace On Earth"

By Sy Miller and Jill Jackson.

(For Organ: Registration No. 7)

"He Ain't Heavy He's My Brother"

Lyric by Bob Russell.
Music by Bobby Scott.

(For Organ: Registration No. 2)

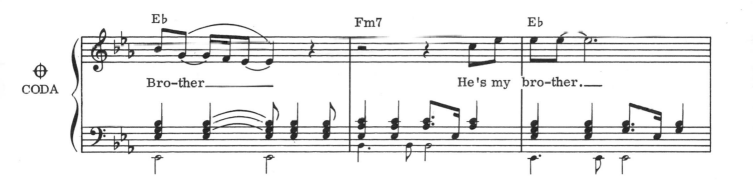

Bro-ther_____ He's my bro-ther.__

He ain't

heavy __ He's my bro-ther He ain't

Repeat and Fade

2. So on we go, his welfare is my concern,
   No burden is he to bear, we'll get there.
   For I know he would not encumber me.
   He ain't heavy, he's my brother.

3. Its a long long road from which there is no return,
   While we're on the way to there, why not share.
   And the load doesn't weigh me down at all.
   He ain't heavy, he's my brother.

"I'll Pray For You"

Written and Composed by
Roy King and Stanley Hill.

(For Organ: Registration No. 3)

.33

"At The End Of The Day"

By Donald O'Keefe.

(For Organ: Registration No. 2)

At the end of the day, Just kneel and say:

"Thank you, Lord, for my work and play; I've tried to be good, for I know that I should." That's a prayer for the end of the day! _____ So

VERSE *(Faster)*

When the new dawn be - gins to break, Just lift up your eyes, let your

"Forgive Me Lord"

Words and Music by Ord Hamilton.

(For Organ: Registration No. 1)

"Morning Has Broken"

Words by Eleanor Farjeon.
Musical arrangement by Cat Stevens.

(For Organ: Registration No. 2)

2. Sweet the rain's new fall, sunlit from heaven,
Like the first dew-fall on the first grass.
Praise for the sweetness of the wet garden,
Sprung in completeness where his feet pass.

3. Mine is the sunlight, mine is the morning,
Born of the one light Eden saw play.
Praise with elation, praise ev'ry morning,
God's recreation of the new day.

4. As first Verse

"Mary's Boy Child"

By Jester Hairston.

(For Organ: Registration No. 5)

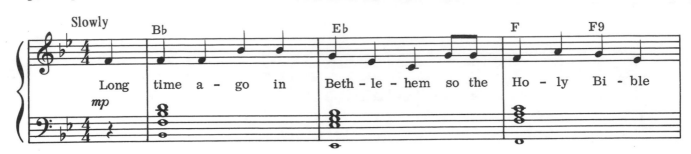

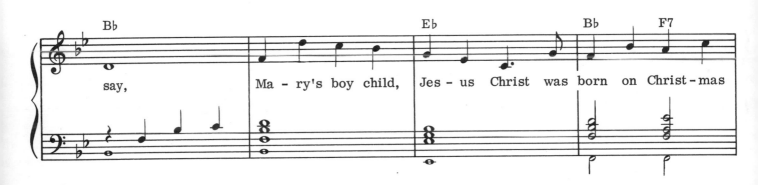

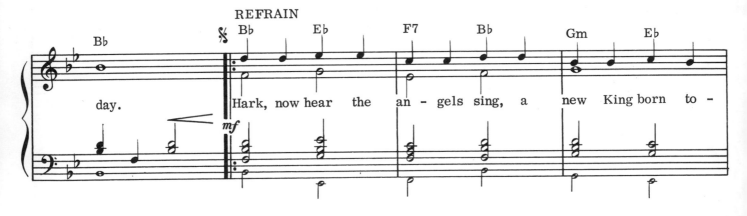

-far, Now Jo - seph and his wife, Ma - ry, Come to
born. Long time a - go in Beth - le - hem, So the

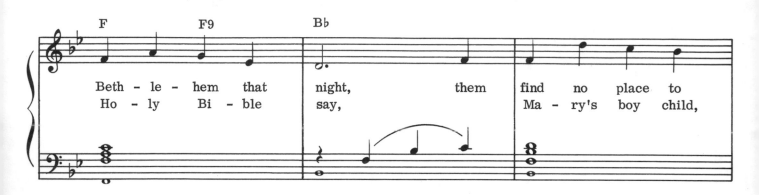

Beth - le - hem that night, them find no place to
Ho - ly Bi - ble say, Ma - ry's boy child,

D. % al Coda

born she child, Not a sin - gle room was in sight.
Je - sus Christ, Was born on Christ mas Day.

CODA

Day Be - cause of Christ-mas Day. _____

"I'll Walk With God"

Words by Paul Francis Webster.
Music by Nicholas Brodszky.

(For Organ: Registration No. 4)

"The Bells Of St. Mary's"

Words by Douglas Furber.
Music by A. Emmett Adams.

(For Organ: Registration No. 5)

REFRAIN (Repeat Both times)

4th time ⊕ to Coda

"If I Can Help Somebody"

Arranged by George L. Zalva.
Music by Alma Androzzo.

(For Organ: Registration No. 4)

"Bless This House"

Words by Helen Taylor.
Music by May H. Brahe.

(For Organ: Registration No. 5)

"The Holy City"

Words by F. E. Weatherly.
Music by Stephen Adams.

(For Organ: Registration No. 3)

"I Walked Into The Garden"

Words by Dale White.
Music by Marion Weaver.

(For Organ: Registration No. 1)

2. I walked into the garden,
My soul was sanctified.
For there it was I knew
That Christ had never died.
I walked out of the garden,
My soul was cleansed of sin,
Oh, yes, I know the reason
It was because of him.

3. Come with me to the garden
And lay your burdens there,
For Jesus knows your sorrows,
Knows your ev'ry care.
Receive His grace and pardon,
Confess your ev'ry sin,
Come with me to the garden
And dwell in peace with Him.

"Oh! Happy Day"

Words and music by
Edwin R. Hawkins.

(For Organ: Registration No. 5)

Registration No.	*Single-Manual Organs	*All Electronic Organs		*All Drawbar Organs	
1	8' 4' I II III	Upper: Lower: Pedal:	Flute 8' Melodia 8' 8', Soft	Upper: Lower: Pedal:	60 8808 000 (00) 5554 433 (1) 4-2 (Spinet 3)
2	8' I II	Upper: Lower: Pedal:	Cello 16', Trumpet 8', Flute 8', 4' Reed 8', Viola 8' (String 8') 16', 8', Full	Upper: Lower: Pedal:	40 8606 005 (00) 4543 222 (1) 4-2 (Spinet 3)
3	8' 2' I III V	Upper: Lower: Pedal:	Flute 16', (Tibia 16'), Clarinet 8', (Reed 8') Diapason 8' 16', Soft	Upper: Lower: Pedal:	60 8805 005 (00) 5544 321 (0) 4-2 (Spinet 3)
4	8' 4' 2' I II III V	Upper: Lower: Pedal:	Flute 16', (Tibia 16'), Flute 8' Diapason 8', Melodia 8' 16', 8' Medium	Upper: Lower: Pedal:	80 8080 800 (00) 6544 444 (2) 4-2 (Spinet 3)
5	8' 4' II	Upper: Lower: Pedal:	Flute 16', (Tibia 16'), Flute 8', Reed 8', Horn 8' Melodia 8', Diapason 8' 16', 8' Full	Upper: Lower: Pedal:	50 8806 006 (00) 5555 443 (3) 4-2 (Spinet 3)
6	8' 4' 2' I II V	Upper: Lower: Pedal:	Flute 16', (Tibia 16'), Flute 8', 4' Diapason 8', Horn 8' 16', 8' Medium	Upper: Lower: Pedal:	00 8080 600 (00) 4433 222 (0) 4-2 (Spinet 3)
7	8' II IV V	Upper: Lower: Pedal:	Diapason 8' Flute 8' 8' Medium	Upper: Lower: Pedal:	60 8008 000 (00) 5544 000 (0) 4-2 (Spinet 3)

* Vibrato and Reverberation left to personal preference

Printed in England by WEST CENTRAL PRINTING CO. LTD., London and Suffolk.